To the best

Daughter

in the world

OUR JOURNAL
of your life

Dear Daughter

I'm giving you this journal so that we can share your memories, precious times, funny stories, embarrassing moments and your hopes and dreams for the future.

Whenever something pops into your head, just scribble a note in the handy sections laid out. We'll have so much fun reviewing them together, and it's bound to prompt more memories.

It doesn't have to be all words – personalise your journal with doodles, sketches and photos. You'll find a pocket at the back where you can safely store postcards, invitations, menus and other scrapbook mementos so they'll never be lost.

I can't wait to share your journal with you.

All about you

The one and only!

What inspires you?

What gets you up in the morning?

What is your first memory? How did you get to be so gorgeous? What makes you giggle? Fill this in so that, one day, you can share it with your own child!

x X x

When I was born, my world was like this…

My first wheels

newsflash!

beautiful baby

Me as a baby

Date of birth:

Place of birth:

Birth weight:

I was named:

My pet name is:

hair colour

eye colour

This is how I'd describe myself...

Me,
aged:

marvellous me!

My vital statistics

Height:

Weight:

Dress size:

Shoe size:

I grew up in a place called…

I've lived in:

my first house

My first home
address

Street:

Town:

County:

My school days were…

_____

_____

_____

_____

_____

_____

_____

_____

_____

_____

_____

_____

_____

_____

_____

_____

_____

_____

_____

_____

favourite book

My best subjects:

school clubs

My worst subjects:

Great teacher:

Terrible teacher:

Best days!

My style guru…

clothes

favourite
shops

shoes

makeup

accessories

In my down time, I like to...

pastime

hobby

exercise

My passion...

Darling, I've finished reading your first chapter, but I would still like to know...

You and Me

Are we alike?

My little treasure!

What do we do for fun?

What's it like being a daughter? Do you like your name? Do you know what your first word was? Do you think we look alike? What's the best thing about being a daughter? I'm so proud of you!

x X x

My first memory is...

You and me ↙

Childhood memories

Favourite storybook

....

Favourite song

....

Favourite toy

....

I remember when…

wobbly tooth

first haircut

first birthday

We are alike…

eye colour

Me aged

We are different…

face shape

Some of the things I like doing with you...

Remember when we...

gardening

cooking

talking on the phone

ride a bicycle

You taught me how to...

_____

_____

_____

_____

_____

_____

_____

_____

_____

_____

_____

_____

Some things my mum taught me
that I'll pass on to my children:

do
first
aid

knit and sew

change a plug

grow your own

I love you, Mum, because…

beautiful

funny

What makes
you so special:

You

clever

kind

helpful

Sweetie, there are a couple of things you missed out that I thought of...

Family and Friends

The support group! ↗

Any family secrets?

Whose shoulder do you cry on?

What do you remember about your grandparents when you were growing up? Do you have a favourite aunt or uncle? Which of your cousins do you feel closest to? How many friends do you have? You can tell me anything!

My family and other animals...

grandpa

grandma

← Taken when...

dad

mum   pets

Taken when...

Siblings can be good company –
they can also be very annoying…

sisters
brothers

List of annoying things...

↑ together

Some of our relations are lovely…

aunties

Notable relations:

Some of our relations are seriously weird...

uncles

Skeleton in the
cupboard...

cousins

we never
mention...

My best ever friend is...

the things we did!

How we laughed!

always looked
out for me

↖ Me and my shadow

a shoulder to cry on

When I'm with the girls…

Best night ever!

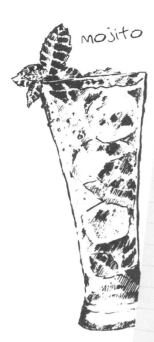
mojito

Where:

When:

Who was there:

our favourite songs

our favourite boxset

My first boyfriend was…

_____

_____

_____

_____

_____

_____

_____

_____

_____

_____

_____

first kiss

photo taken in:

split up!

He was aged:

I was aged:

We were friends for:

fun memories

This is hilarious, but you may have missed a few people from the family tree...

Life's Highlights

The story so far!

What are the high points?

Who did you share them with?

Have you ever fallen in love? What's the most breathtaking place you've ever visited? Have you ever felt really proud of yourself? Share your special moments.

x X x

My soul mate…

_____

_____

_____

_____

_____

_____

_____

_____

_____

Love at first sight!

He said to me:

I said to him:

The happiest Christmas I enjoyed...

Christmas tree

white Christmas

mistletoe

_____

_____

_____

_____

_____

_____

_____

_____

_____

_____

_____

_____

_____

_____

_____

_____

_____

_____

_____

_____

_____

_____

A very
Merry →
Christmas

My best holiday ever…

_____

_____

_____

_____

_____

_____

_____

Paradise!

sun, sea, sand

romantic
city breaks

The best parties, gigs and festivals of my life…

Party-goers:

hip-hop

regular tipple

I must remember never to...

My wedding day…

Guest List

You are invited to
The Wedding of

....

&

....

on

....

at

....

The
happy
couple!
←

ding! dong!

The day my baby, your grandchild, was born...

birthday cake

special gifts

New baby

Date of birth:

Place of birth:

Birth weight:

Named:

Notes:

birthday cards

What are the golden moments you're still looking forward to, angel?

Prizes and Trophies

And the winner is...

The golden child!

Do you remember what you won at school? Have you kept your badges? What's the bravest thing you've ever done? Show everyone your passport photos!

x X x

The greatest triumphs of my life are…

_____

_____

_____

_____

_____

_____

_____

_____

_____

_____

_____

_____

_____

_____

moving away from home

Life events

First job ☐

First flat ☐

First bill ☐

First house ☐

Engagement ☐

Marriage ☐

First baby ☐

travelling
alone

I'm really good at...

dancing

Best in class!

egg and spoon race

making muffins

I've won prizes for...

best costume

raffle
tombola

beautiful
baby

Well done me!
↓

Karaoke

CERTIFICATE

This has been awarded to

The bravest thing I've ever done...

sticking up
for a friend

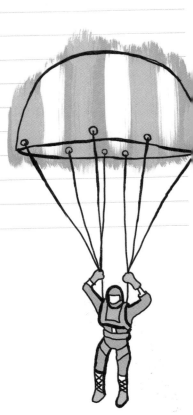

apologise

rescue mission

I did it!

I'm still a tiny bit scared of...

I've set myself a target to...

_____

_____

_____

_____

_____

_____

_____

_____

_____

_____

_____

Reminder...

exercise
regularly

TO DO List...

I never thought I'd be able to…

That's me! ➚

learn a language

volunteer

perform in public

Daughter, I think you've been a bit modest
– there are lots of other accomplishments
you haven't mentioned...

Dramas and dilemmas

Life's a lottery!

A & E

A.S.A.P

OMG!

Were you ever a daredevil or a diva? Did you ever get into scrapes? What's the worst accident you've ever had? Have you ever missed an important appointment? Tell me about your mishaps.

My worst holiday nightmare was…

hopelessly lost!

storms ahead

sunburn

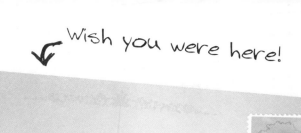

Wish you were here!

Dear

Love from

I can't believe I said that...!

it wasn't me!

Top 10 embarrassing moments:

putting your foot in it!

coughing
fit

I'll never live it down!

Did I ever tell you about the time…?

My rescue!

spilt milk

accidents &
emergencies

not again!

I can't believe I got away with it...

wardrobe malfunctio

makeup glitch

message deleted!

sent mail

Work disasters:

Who:

When:

What:

I'm only telling you about this so
you don't make the same mistakes…

Missed appointments

Getting lost

Money Mistakes

I wish I hadn't...

who to trust

Some things make me sad…

departures

Always on
my mind ↳

Dear girl, it's good to know that, whatever happens, you've always overcome it. How do you think it might have changed you?

green tea or latte?

Favourite Stuff

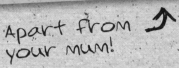
Apart from your mum! ↗

Robert Pattinson or Richard Madden?

Who's your favourite DJ?
Which actress do you admire most?
What's the best book you've ever read?
Vanilla or chocolate? Kitten or puppy?
Long skirt or short skirt? I'd like to
know all your secret desires.

x X x

My favourite band is…

_____

_____

_____

_____

_____

_____

_____

_____

best instrument

most popular song

Best festival ever!

My favourite film is...

costume drama

who dunnit?

rom-com

Top ten films...

action adventure

My favourite author is…

Must-read books…

Virginia Woolf

Maya Angelou

Charlotte Bronte

Jane Austen

Agatha Christie

My favourite food is…

chocolate gateau

Meal out!

sushi
and sake

strawberries
and champagne

breakfast in bed

My favourite place is…

home sweet home

So lovely!

I couldn't live without…

pet

tea coffee

treats

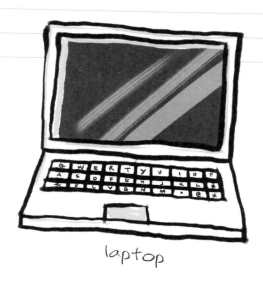

laptop

Now I know some of your favourites things, do you have a secret wish list of things you've always wanted but never had?

Philosophy of life

And other theories! ↗

Whatever will be will be!

That's life!

What is your viewpoint on life? Do you have a catchphrase? Are there any sayings that help you through difficult moments? Who do you turn to when you need a mentor? Let me in on your wise thoughts!

x X x

My philosophy of life is…

Keep smiling!

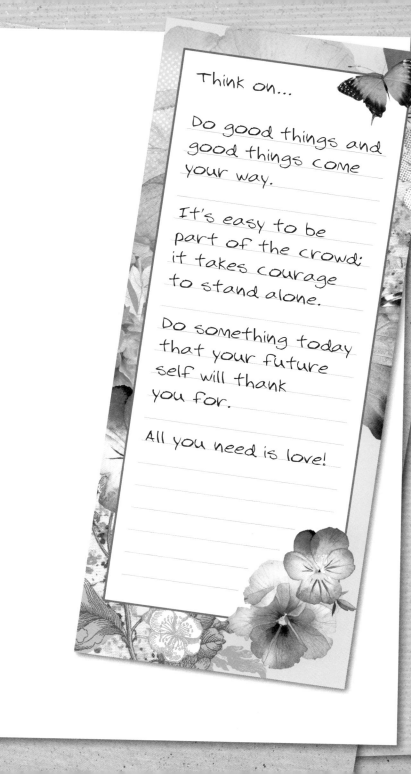

Think on...

Do good things and good things come your way.

It's easy to be part of the crowd; it takes courage to stand alone.

Do something today that your future self will thank you for.

All you need is love!

The world would be a better place if...

abolish
exams

ban size 0

leave the toilet
seat down

no litter

recycle

My pet rants...

stop global warming
end poverty

Some of the proverbs and sayings that help me…

Two wrongs don't make a right.

✚ ✖ ✓

It's not the years in your life that count, it's the life in your years.

Laugh and the world laughs with you.

You learn from your mistakes.

My favourite expressions…

Hilarious tweets:

Whatever!

Boxset
and chill!

Awesome!

Did I do that?!

If life has taught me anything, it's…

Sometimes, I AM right!

Every day is a
new beginning.

Beauty is only
skin deep.

Think before
you speak!

These are the values I've learnt from you...

Life lessons:

Be truthful

face new challenges

Put others first

Make amends

kindness
courage
honesty
loyalty
patience

My lovely daughter, I never knew you were such a philosopher! What's the single most useful advice for life you will carry with you?

Bucket List

TO DO list!

action plan

hopes and dreams

Tell me about the things you'd like to do. What places would you like to visit? Are there any new activities you'd like to try? Be photographed on the red carpet? Watch wildlife from a hot air balloon? Live life to the full!

x X x

These are the places I'd most love to visit…

Itch list:

Rome
Barcelona
Prague
Amsterdam
Dublin
Paris

I'd like to try my hand at...

potter's wheel

juggling

surfing

half marathon

yarn bombing

I did it!

↳

I'm determined to learn …

first aid

highway code

Italian French Spanish German Japanese

orienteering

baking
sourdough
bread

My personal goals are…

_____

_____

_____

_____

_____

_____

_____

_____

_____

_____

_____

_____

_____

be happy

learn to relax

My goal schedule:

Together we can…

_____
_____
_____
_____
_____
_____
_____
_____
_____
_____
_____

Activities for two:

stronger
together

Dear

Love,
your daughter
x

PULTENEY
PRESS

First published by Pulteney Press in 2017
Copyright © Pulteney Press 2017

Written by Katherine Sully • Illustrated by Michael Cheung
All other images 123rf

ISBN 978-1-78718-681-1

Printed in China